boyzone said

wise publications
london / new york / paris / sydney / copenhagen / madrid

Exclusive Distributors:
Music Sales Limited
8/9 Frith Street, London W1V 5TZ, England.

Music Sales Pty Limited
120 Rothschild Avenue, Rosebery, NSW 2018, Australia.

Order No. AM934681
ISBN 0-7119-5453-4
This book © Copyright 1995 by Wise Publications.

Book design by Michael Bell Design.
Music arranged by Roger Day.
Music processed by Paul Ewers Music Design.

Printed in the United Kingdom by
Halstan & Co. Ltd., Amersham, Bucks.

Your Guarantee of Quality:
As publishers, we strive to produce every book to the highest
commercial standards. Whilst endeavouring to retain the original running order
of the recorded album, the book has been carefully designed to minimise
awkward page turns and to make playing from it a real pleasure.
Particular care has been given to specifying acid-free, neutral-sized
paper made from pulps which have not been elemental chlorine bleached.
This pulp is from farmed sustainable forests and was produced with
special regard for the environment.
Throughout, the printing and binding have been planned to ensure
a sturdy, attractive publication which should give years of enjoyment.
If your copy fails to meet our high standards, please inform us and
we will gladly replace it.

Music Sales' complete catalogue describes thousands of titles and is
available in full colour sections by subject, direct from Music Sales Limited.
Please state your areas of interest and send a cheque/postal order
for £1.50 for postage to: Music Sales Limited,
Newmarket Road, Bury St. Edmunds, Suffolk IP33 3YB.

boyzone

Together

Words & Music by Martin Brannigan, Ronan Keating & Ray Hedges

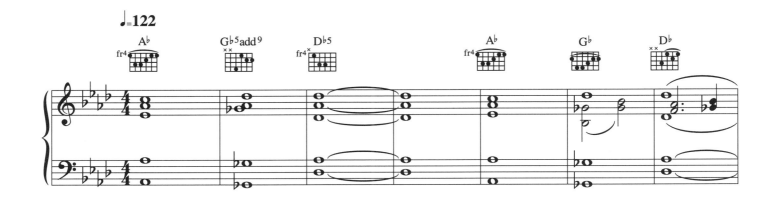

To - geth - er, _____ it's bet - ter by far, _____ that's where we are, _____ you'll see. _____

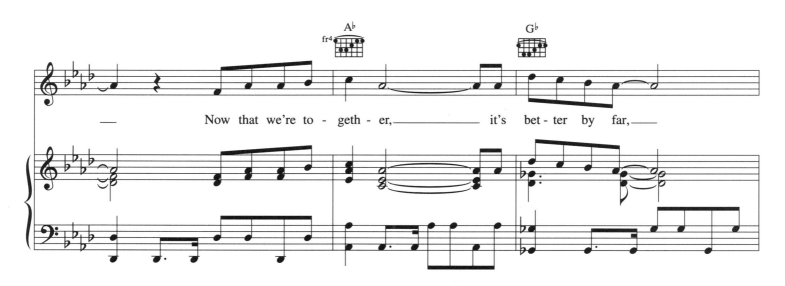

_____ Now that we're to - geth - er, _____ it's bet - ter by far, _____

that's where we are,_____ you'll see._____ 1. Don't hold me up, I'm mov-ing
(Verse 2 see block lyric)

out; ev-'ry-where I go, you al-ways block my road. I'm on that

train,_____ where will it go? North,— East, West or South, found—

—— by word of mouth. Oh, we've_____ got to change— the way— we feel——

that's where we are,___ you'll see.___ Now that we're to-___

I some-times lose___ my-self___ for e-ter-ni-ty,___ yeah.

I find my way___ back some-how, and face the plain___ re-al-i-ty.___ To-

ge-ther,___ it's bet-ter by far,___ that's what we are,___ you'll see.___

Now that we're to - ge - ther,_____ it's bet - ter by far,_____

that's what we are,_____ you'll see._____ Now that we're to - ge - ther,_____ to-

ge - ther,_____ that's what we are,_____ you'll see._____ Now that we're to -

Play 4 times
Begin fade 3rd time

Verse 2:
When we were small, they always said
We would be together, always and forever.
Then you changed your pretty way;
I will take it no more,
My feet ain't stuck to the floor.

Love Me For A Reason

Words & Music by John Bristol, Wade Brown Jr & David Jones Jr

1. Girl, when you hold me,
(Verses 2 & 3 see block lyric)

how you con-trol me; you bend and you fold me an-y way you please.

To Coda ⊕

11

let the rea - son be love.

D.%. al Coda

⊕ *Coda*

Don't love me for fun,— girl, let me be— the one, girl, love me for a rea - son,

let the rea - son be love. Don't love me for fun,— girl, let me be— the one, girl;

Verse 2:
Kisses and caresses are only minor tests, babe,
Of love needs and stresses between a woman and a man.
So if love everlasting isn't what you're asking,
I'll have to pass, girl; I'm proud to take a stand.
I can't continue guessing, because it's only messing
With my pride and my mind.
So write down this time to time:

To Chorus

Verse 3:
I'm just a little old-fashioned,
It takes more than a physical attraction.
My initial reaction is "Honey, give me love;
Not a facsimile of."

To Chorus

Coming Home Now

**Words & Music by Stephen Gately, Ronan Keating,
Michael Graham, Shane Lynch & Keith Duffy**

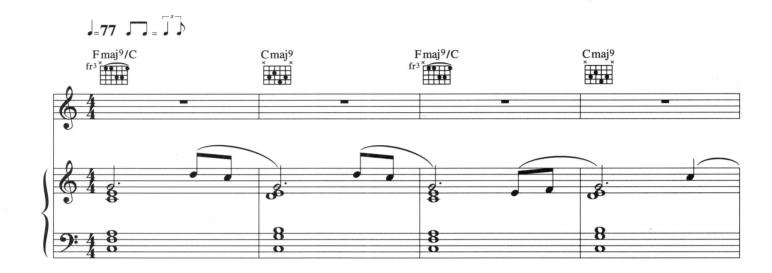

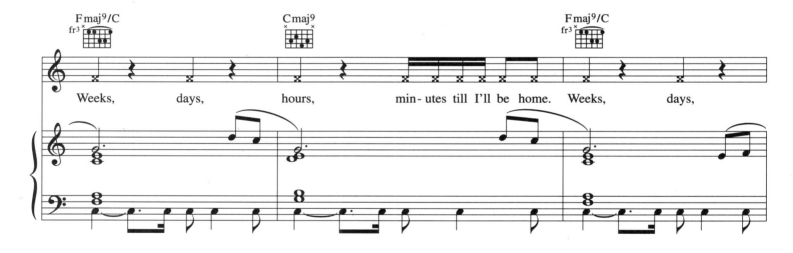

D.%. al Coda

I did-n't leave in vain.— And there's a

⊕ Coda

— now,——— it's been so long— now.——— Gon-na get there some-

- how,——— and this is where I'll stay,————— and this is where I'll

stay.———

Spoken: "Dearly close words: I really want to see you. You're in my heart when overseas.
I feel you close, and not so far. Soon we'll be together, and this time it's forever.

I'm

When All Is Said And Done

Words & Music by Martin Brannigan, Stephen Gately, Ronan Keating, Michael Graham, Shane Lynch, Keith Duffy & Ray Hedges

1. Days that we spent when I was so small,
(Verse 2 see block lyric)
ne-ver let me fall, you ne-ver let me fall.

Taught me to see ___ the right and the wrong; ___ oh, I'm not that strong, ___ wish I was that strong. ___ You've been good ___ to me, tend-ing my ev - 'ry need. Just look ___ what I am, ___

Verse 2:
Now I'm a man, time has gone fast;
I didn't want it to, I didn't want it to.
Went on my way like a crazy young fool;
I never wanted to, I never wanted to.
You've been good *etc.*

Oh Carol

Words & Music by Clive Scott, Desmond Dyer & Ray Hedges

1. I've got to tell you, girl you're in dan - ger. ____
(Verse 2 see block lyric).

No-one can save you now; you're gon - na be mine some-how.

Ca - rol, _____ got - ta make you mine; Ca - rol _____ it - 'll work out fine.

I know it's love, I know it's love for real. I know it's love, I know the way I feel.

Ca - rol, _____ you're my dream come true, Ca - rol, _____ when I look at you;

Ca - rol, say you'll ne - ver go, Ca - rol, now I need you so.

26

Verse 2:
Can't you feel it, it's all around you;
Reach out and take it all,
Don't be afraid to fall.
Don't want to lose you, now that I've found you;
I'll always be around, I'll never let you down.

I loved you long ago *etc.*

So Good

Words & Music by Martin Brannigan, Stephen Gately, Ronan Keating,
Michael Graham, Shane Lynch, Keith Duffy & Ray Hedges

Coda ⊕

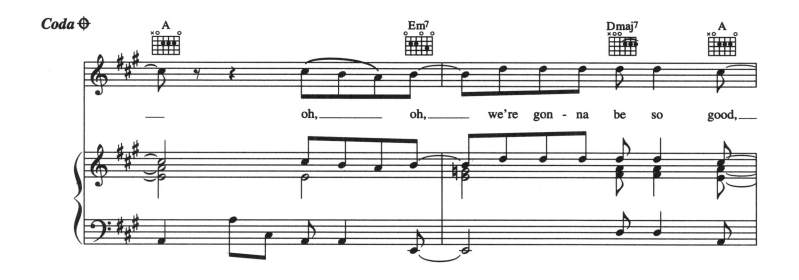

oh,_____ oh,_____ we're gon - na be so good,___

___ like I knew we would,_____ you know we're good._____

Verse 2:
No matter the cost
When we're out on the town getting lazy
I'll show you who's boss
We're just gonna take it all the way
No matter what they say now.

Can't Stop Me

Words & Music by Martin Brannigan, Stephen Gately & Ray Hedges

35

Verse 2:
All my advice, I give it to thee;
So take my heart and treat it honestly.
If you don't take what I have for you,
You'll never know what you're gonna lose.

Oh, I may have done wrong *etc.*

I'll Be There

**Words & Music by Martin Brannigan, Tony Jackson,
Jeffrey Sayadian & Ray Hedges**

1. Day and night I'm think-ing of
(Verse 2 see block lyric)

you, with a heart that is true;— on-ly you can have the feel-ing too.

Verse 2:
Deep inside, I suddenly knew
It had to be you;
Oh I tried to stay, stay away.
The dream I had was never to be;
All I could see
There inside, my foolish pride.
Something special I'll say *etc.*

Key To My Life

Words & Music by Martin Brannigan, Stephen Gately,
Ronan Keating, Michael Graham, & Ray Hedges

miss- ing you so___ and I won't let you go___ a - way.___

And I nev - er gave___ up hope___ when things got___ me down;___ but I

just bit on___ my lip___ and my face be - gan___ to frown.___ 'Cos

that was just___ my pride,___ and I've no - thing left___ to hide,___ and

45

now the way is clear, and all I want to say is:

All of my life the doors have been closed now, and all of my dreams have been

locked up in-side. But you came a-long and cap-tured my heart, girl,

you're the key to my life.

To Coda ⊕

46

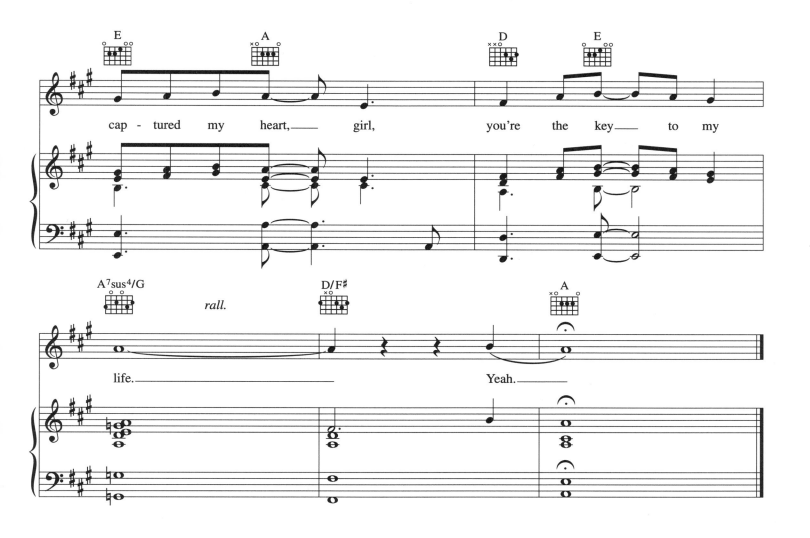

cap - tured my heart,＿＿ girl, you're the key＿＿ to my

life.＿＿＿＿＿＿＿＿＿＿＿ Yeah.＿＿＿

rall.

Verse 2:
Stain on the desktop where coffee cup lay,
And memories of you forever will stay;
And the scent of your perfume,
And the smile on your face will remain.

Verse 3:
Year after year, was blaming myself
For what I'd done; just thought of myself.
I know that you'll understand
This was all my own fault — don't go away.

If You Were Mine

Words & Music by Andy Hill & Joey Balin

I see what he's doin' to you, and it hurts me so;

I wish I could steal you a-way, but you just won't go.

Some-thing's hold-ing you close to him some-thing I can't see

but, come the day that you've had e - nough, — I pray you come run - ning to

me. _____ 'Cause if you were mine, —

you'd know how good love can be. _____ And if you were mine, —

I'd love you e - ter - nal - ly; _____

ba - by, it's___ as sad___ as it___ can be._____

'Cause if you were mine,___ you'd know how good love can be.___

___ And if you were mine,___

I'd love you e - ter - nal - ly,___ if you were mine,—

you'd know how good love can be.

And if you were mine,

I'd love you e-ter-nal-ly, if you were mine.

57

Arms Of Mary

Words & Music by Iain Sutherland

Verse 2:
She took the pains of boyhood,
And turned them into feel good;
Oh, and how I wish I was
Lying in the arms of Mary.

Believe In Me

**Words & Music by Martin Brannigan, Stephen Gately,
Ronan Keating, Mark Taylor, Paul Holgate & Ray Hedges**

1. I've been tak-ing all my time_____ could I be blind?
(Verse 2 see block lyric)

Hey, I'm kin-da feel-in' that there's just one rea-son why_____

Verse 2:
All the mountains that we climb, day at a time;
I promise you no heartache,
Nothing left to hide
Swallow my pride.
Guess you're not believing
I'm turning the tide.
'Cos I can't eat *etc.*

Father And Son

Words & Music by Cat Stevens

$\, = 72$

1. It's not

time to make a change; just re-lax, take it ea-sy. You're still

(Verse 2 see block lyric)

young, that's your fault; there's so much you have to know. Find a girl,

set - tle down;___ if you want,___ you___ can mar - ry. Look at me:___

1. I am old___ but I'm hap - py. 2. I was

2. ___ be here___ to - mor - row,___ but your dreams may not.

How can I___ try to ex - plain?___ When I do___

(Verse 4 see block lyric)

To Coda ⊕

D.%. al Coda

I am old___ but I'm hap - py.   4. All the

Coda

have to go___ a - way.___   I know ___   I have_ to   go.

Verse 2:

I was once like you are now;
And I know that it's not easy
To be calm when you've found something going on.
But take your time, think a lot;
Think of everything you've got.
For you will still be here tomorrow,
But your dreams may not.

Verse 4:

All the times that I've cried,
Keeping all the things I knew inside;
And it's hard, but it's harder to ignore it.
If they were right I'd agree,
But it's them they know, not me;
Now there's a way, and I know
That I have to go away.
I know I have to go.